This book is for a special girl,
Fairy sparkles shine and swirl,
Turn the page and take a peep,
So much to read, enjoy and keep!

Let's get ready, take our hand,
Fly with us to Fairyland!
Spells and magic wait inside,
Fairy friends will be your guide.

This
Rainbow Magic
Ultimate Fairy
Annual belongs to:

....

ORCHARD BOOKS
338 Euston Road, London NW1 3BH
Orchard Books Australia
Level 17/207 Kent Street, Sydney, NSW 2000

First published in 2014 by Orchard Books

A CIP catalogue record for this book is available from the British Library.

ISBN 978 1 40833 376 1

1 3 5 7 9 10 8 6 4 2

Printed in China

The paper and board used in this paperback are natural recyclable products made from wood grown in sustainable forests.
The manufacturing processes conform to the environmental regulations of the country of origin.

Orchard Books is a division of Hachette Children's Books, an Hachette UK company

www.hachette.co.uk

Adult supervision is recommended when glue, paint, scissors and other sharp points are in use,
and for activities that require cooking, baking or heating.

The Ultimate Fairy Annual 2015

Fabulous fairies are waiting
for you inside!

Contents

Dear Fairy Friend,

Welcome to our enchanting new Rainbow Magic Annual — we are thrilled to see you! This 2015 edition is shimmering with so much magic, Scarlett the Garnet Fairy had to cast a special shrinking spell to fit everything inside.

The book is full of puzzles, games and colouring fun, plus a brand new Rainbow Magic story. You really are in for a treat! We Magical Crafts Fairies have even added a few of our favourite make-its for you to try.

Enjoy your new Annual — it's especially for you!

With happy hugs and fairy giggles,

Kayla x Annabelle x Zadie x Josie x Violet x Libby x Roxie x

What Kind of Fairy are You?

There are so many beautiful fairies, but which one are you most like? Answer the questions and work your way down the flowchart. Your true fairy type will be revealed!

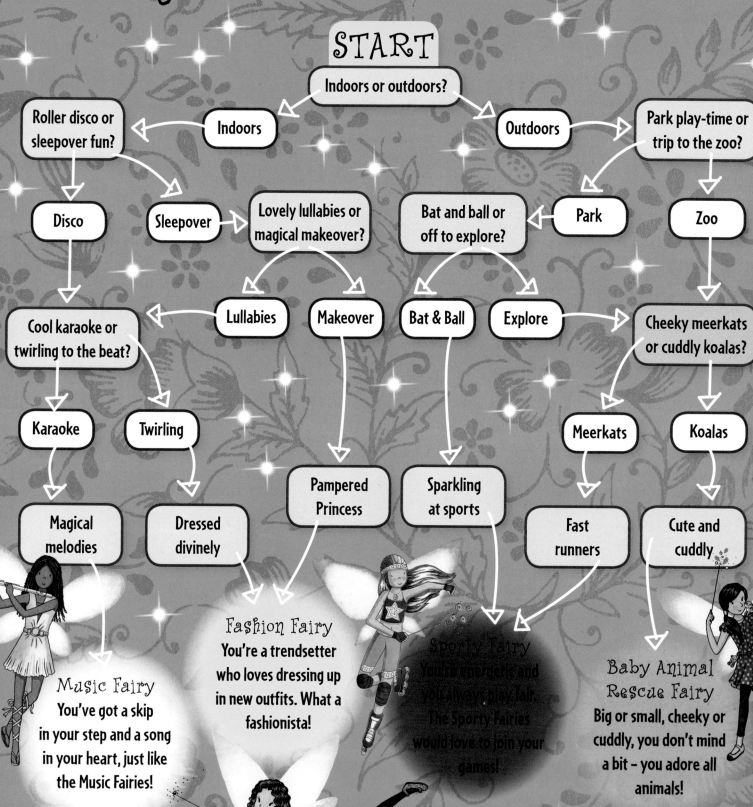

START

Indoors or outdoors?

Indoors → Outdoors

Roller disco or sleepover fun? ← Indoors

Outdoors → Park play-time or trip to the zoo?

Disco — Sleepover → Lovely lullabies or magical makeover?

Bat and ball or off to explore? ← Park

Zoo

Cool karaoke or twirling to the beat?

Lullabies — Makeover

Bat & Ball — Explore

Cheeky meerkats or cuddly koalas?

Karaoke — Twirling

Meerkats — Koalas

Magical melodies — Dressed divinely

Pampered Princess

Sparkling at sports

Fast runners — Cute and cuddly

Music Fairy
You've got a skip in your step and a song in your heart, just like the Music Fairies!

Fashion Fairy
You're a trendsetter who loves dressing up in new outfits. What a fashionista!

Sporty Fairy
You're energetic and you always play fair. The Sporty Fairies would love to join your games!

Baby Animal Rescue Fairy
Big or small, cheeky or cuddly, you don't mind a bit – you adore all animals!

Pop Star Puzzle

Oh dear! Destiny the Pop Star Fairy has got dressed up for a photoshoot, but something has gone wrong with the pictures. Only one of these snaps perfectly matches the original. Can you spot which one it is?

A

B

C

D

Find out if you're right on Page 61

9

Meet Kayla the Pottery Fairy

It's such fun to make pottery presents for my fairy friends!

Personality
Kind and creative.

Favourite fairy friend
Willow the Wednesday Fairy.

Magical object
A tiny ceramic vase.

Best crafts project
A sparkly sculpture of Queen Titania!

Favourite place in Fairyland
The pottery workshop at the back of her toadstool house.

Most trusted magic
When Kayla's around, everyone can enjoy making things with clay.

Fairy outfit
Kayla likes to belt in her favourite denim dress and roll up her sleeves. She loves her super-cute pink headband and espadrilles. Add a pair of cropped leggings and her look is complete!

Rainspell Island's Crafts Week got off to a terrible start when a goblin trapped Kayla in a clay jar! Luckily Kirsty and Rachel were there to rescue the frightened Pottery Fairy.

Kayla's Lovely Letters

Have you ever tried modelling with salt dough? Let Kayla show you how! You don't need a pottery workshop – anyone can make these letters at home and bake them in the oven.

You will need:
- [ ] 500g flour
- [ ] 300g salt
- [ ] 250ml water
- [ ] Old newspapers
- [ ] Poster paint
- [ ] Paintbrush
- [ ] PVA glue
- [ ] Glitter
- [ ] Clear varnish

1
Use a wooden spoon to mix the flour, salt and water together in a bowl. If the salt dough looks too dry and crumbly, tip in a little more water and stir.

2
When the mixture becomes a gooey lump, take it out and knead it with your hands. Now you're ready to start modelling!

Ask a grown-up to heat the oven to 180°C/350°F/ Gas Mark 4.

3
Pull off a piece of dough and shape it into a letter. You could make your initials or even spell out your name. Gently lay each finished letter onto a baking tray.

4
Bake the letters in the oven for about 1 hour. When hardened, ask a grown-up to take them out and cool them on a wire rack.

5
Over some old newspapers, paint each letter in a bright colour. Make sure that the whole shape is covered, on both sides.

6
When the paint is dry, dot some PVA glue over the letters and sprinkle glitter over the top. Then add a layer of clear varnish to make the letters really gleam.

7
Your sparkly letters are ready to put on display! Use them to jazz up a bookshelf, or wrap them in tissue and surprise a friend.

Why not glue a magnet to the back of each letter and display them on the fridge?

FAIRIES

Part 1

Diamonds and Ice

"Can you see it?" asked Kirsty Tate, using her glove to make a circle in the misty car window. "Look up there!"

Rachel Walker peeped out and smiled. Just ahead of them, a majestic deer was standing on the hillside.

"It must be a stag," she exclaimed.

The best friends were in a car with their parents, driving through Scotland. It was New Year's Eve and the families had booked a week together in a holiday cottage.

"I can't wait to celebrate the new year with you," said Kirsty, reaching for Rachel's hand.

Rachel felt very lucky, too. When she was with Kirsty, magical things seemed to happen! They had already shared lots of adventures with the Rainbow Magic Fairies. She wondered when they'd see them next.

The holiday cottage was just as pretty as it had looked in Mrs Tate's brochure. The white brick building sat in a valley, surrounded by heather. Frost dusted the purple flowers, making them twinkle in the sun.

Kirsty and Rachel wheeled their cases into a cosy, wood-panelled bedroom. Two snuggly-looking beds stood next to each other.

"It's perfect," decided Rachel, flopping down on the nearest one.

"So…" said Kirsty. "What are your new year's resolutions, Rachel?"

Rachel's eyes twinkled.

"I only have one," she whispered. "Next year, I'm determined to have another fairy adventure!"

Tap-tap-tap!

Kirsty and Rachel stared at each other. The sound came again.

Tap-tap-tap!

"Look at the window," said Kirsty. "It's snowing outside."

Rachel gasped. It wasn't just snow – it was Chrissie the Wish Fairy and Gabriella the Snow Kingdom Fairy, tapping on the window!

She rushed over to let them in, amidst a flurry of fairy dust.

"Thanks!" cried Chrissie, dusting down her fur-trimmed dress.

"It's lovely to see you again," beamed Gabriella. A tiny stream of snowflakes cascaded out of her wand, disappearing into the winter air.

The girls and fairies were thrilled to see each other. But after Chrissie had shared all the Fairyland news, her smile suddenly faded.

"We've come to ask a favour," she explained. "There's an important job that must be done before midnight. We'd need to shrink you both to fairy size – if you wouldn't mind?"

Kirsty and Rachel's cheeks flushed with excitement.

"We don't mind," gushed Rachel. "We don't mind at all!"

Turn to page 38 to find out what happens to Kirsty and Rachel next!

Wand Wordsearch

Ruby's wand is very special. It makes tiny scarlet flowers. What do the other fairies' wands make? This wordsearch is hiding the answers. Look at each fairy picture, then write in the special thing that appears at the end of their wands.

Morgan the Midnight Fairy

_____

Natalie the Christmas Stocking Fairy

_____

Emma the Easter Fairy

_____

Miranda the Beauty Fairy

_____

Fern the Green Fairy

_____

Lucy the Diamond Fairy

_____

Alexa
the Fashion
Reporter Fairy

_____

Summer
the Holiday
Fairy

_____

Before a fairy earns her wand, she has to learn all of her spells off by heart.

Did you know that every fairy's wand is magically made?

E A S T E R E G G N

D G N I N T H G I L

R I B F T C W G U K

Y P A X S H E L L C

I E D M N M K D E I

L N H V O L D C P T

R O X A Z N B L T S

H E A R T L D O V P

J Z K W Q S G C F I

S N O W F L A K E L

Find out if you're right on Page 61

Leah
the Theatre
Fairy

_____

Storm the
Lightning
Fairy

_____

15

Healthy, Happy Days

Do you eat good, healthy food? Megan the Monday Fairy makes sure that she has lots of fruit and vegetables every single day. Here are some fairy-fabulous tips for spreading the mealtime magic...

Go green!

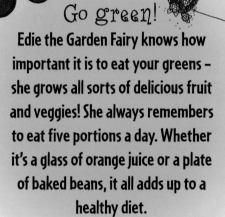

Edie the Garden Fairy knows how important it is to eat your greens – she grows all sorts of delicious fruit and veggies! She always remembers to eat five portions a day. Whether it's a glass of orange juice or a plate of baked beans, it all adds up to a healthy diet.

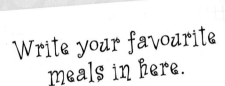

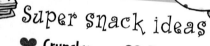

Super snack ideas

- ❤ Crunchy vegetables and dip
- ❤ Raisins
- ❤ Cheese triangles and oatcakes
- ❤ Fruit salad
- ❤ Fromage frais
- ❤ Peanut butter on celery
- ❤ Dried apricots and banana slices
- ❤ Slices of malt loaf

Write your favourite meals in here.

Snack-happy

Even fairies sometimes get hungry between meals! Charlotte the Sunflower Fairy nibbles on a handful of sunflower seeds whenever she feels peckish. What about you?

Food on the go

Elisa the Adventure Fairy loves exploring, but that doesn't stop her eating wholesome, yummy things! She makes mini sandwiches then presses them out with a cookie cutter.

Sweet treats

Lizzie the Sweet Treats Fairy is always tempting her friends with delicious makes and bakes. She just loves sweet things! This dessert recipe is both healthy and delicious.

Elisa's top flavours

❤ Hummus and grated carrot
❤ Turkey and Swiss cheese
❤ Prawn and avocado
❤ Grated apple, cheese and spring onion
❤ Tuna and egg

Ask a grown-up to heat the oven to 180°C/350°F/ Gas Mark 4.

Lizzie's fairy bread pudding

You will need:
❤ 2 tbsp margarine
❤ 6 slices fruit bread
❤ 75g dried apricots
❤ 2 eggs
❤ 1 tsp vanilla extract
❤ 450ml semi-skimmed milk

Have you tried any of these yummy sandwiches?

1. Grease a baking dish with some of the margarine, then spread the rest on the bread slices. Cut each slice into four triangles, and layer in rows in the baking dish.

What delicious dish would you magic up for your friends?

2. Carefully slice the apricots into little pieces and sprinkle them over the bread.

3. Crack the eggs into a mixing bowl, then mix in the vanilla extract and the milk. Pour the mixture over the bread in the baking dish, then cover it with plastic food wrap.

Fast fairy food

A surprise visit from a friend always makes Madison the Magic Fairy smile. She can magic up a host of delicious meals at the drop of a hat! Her favourites are chicken stir-fry and homemade fish fingers.

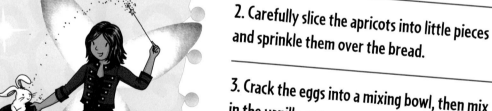

Always ask a grown-up before trying a new recipe. Stay safe in the kitchen.

4. When the milk has soaked into the bread for at least 30 minutes, it's ready to go into the oven. Take off the food wrap and bake it for 40 minutes.

My drawings are simply spellbinding!

Meet Annabelle the Drawing Fairy

Personality
Giggly and bright.

Favourite fairy friend
Keira the Film Star Fairy.

Magical object
A shimmery silver pencil sharpener.

Best crafts project
A portrait of Kirsty and Rachel.

Most trusted magic
When Annabelle waves her wand, fairies and humans draw their very best.

Favourite place in Fairyland
The beach on Rainspell Island. It's the best place to sit and sketch!

Fairy outfit
Annabelle always looks as pretty as a picture! Her rolled-up jeans go beautifully with her fashionable fairy brogues. Violet the Painting Fairy helped her make her colourful tie-dye top.

Drawings everywhere were ruined when the goblins stole Annabelle's pencil sharpener. It took a chase through a garden maze and some daring fairy doodles to get it back again!

Annabelle's Perfect Portrait

Don't forget to sign your magical masterpiece!

Do you love to draw and doodle? Try sketching this picture of Mia the Bridesmaid Fairy. Annabelle will show you what to do! Carefully copy each square from the colour picture into the matching square opposite. Mia will magically appear! When you're finished, bring the portrait to life with coloured pens or pencils.

What's in Belle's Bag?

What do fairies carry in their handbags? Would you like to see? Belle the Birthday Fairy has emptied out her golden clutch bag. Look at the enchanted objects for one minute, then cover this page and try to complete the quiz on the right.

Belle's Quiz!

It's time to put your fairy spotting skills to the test! Find a pen or pencil, then work your way though the quiz.

1. What colour was Belle's birthday candle?

_____

2. Who were shown in the photo?

_____

3. What things does Belle keep in her bag to make her look pretty?

_____

4. What picture was on the front of the birthday book?

_____

5. What was stitched on Belle's pretty handkerchief?

_____

6. What was stored inside the glass bottle?

_____

7. What colour was the bow on Belle's magical birthday present?

_____

8. How many objects were there inside Belle's clutch bag?

_____

Find out if you're right on Page 61

What's in Your Bag?

Do you have a special handbag or satchel? What do you keep inside? It's always useful to carry a few essentials when you go out and about. Take a look at this list, then tick off which things you would use the most.

Handbag List

☐ A pack of tissues
☐ Hand sanitiser
☐ A pretty compact mirror
☐ Hair clips
☐ A travel sewing kit
☐ Perfume

21

Cross Words

Jack Frost is looking grumpy again! He told his goblins to complete his crossword page, but the silly things don't know where to begin! Can you lend a hand? Read each clue, then write the correct answer in the crossword grid.

Across

3. Jack Frost's beloved pet bird.
5. The greedy servants that work for Jack Frost.
7. A frozen garden feature in Jack's castle grounds.
8. Goblins walk with a big pair of these.
9. A hanging spike of frozen water.

Down

1. Jack Frost wears this instead of a coat.
2. Jack's unwelcoming home.
4. The only goblin shade.
6. The colour of Jack's frost-trimmed robes.
8. The magical creatures that Jack can't stand.

Find out if you're right on Page 61

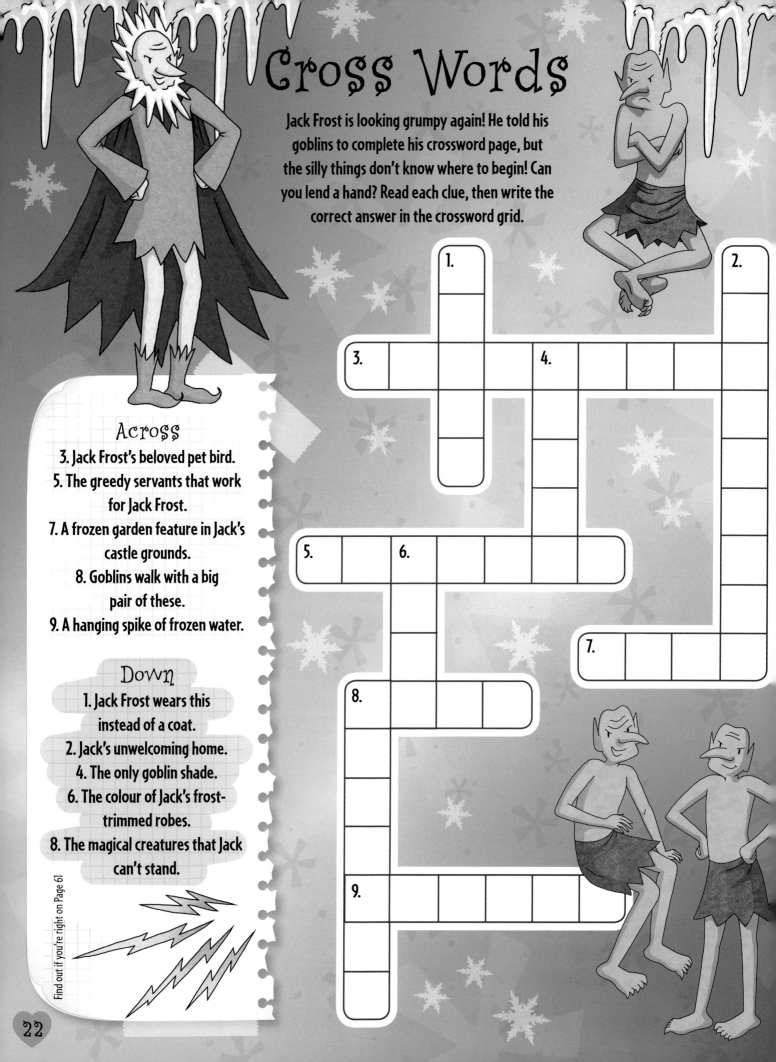

Summer by Numbers

Summer the Holiday Fairy likes to make a splash in zingy colours and fabulous fairy clothes! Can you colour her outfit in all the right shades? Use the key to help you.

Colour key
1 = Yellow
2 = Golden blonde
3 = Orange
4 = Bright pink
5 = Pale pink
6 = Cream

Spells and Goblins

Have you ever played Spells and Goblins? It's the Rainbow Fairies' favourite game! All you need are some counters, a die and someone to play with. Who can get to the top of the board first?

How to play
♥ Choose a counter each, then throw the die. The person with the highest score gets to start first.

❤ Take turns to work your way up the board. If you land at the bottom of a trail of fairy stars, swoosh your counter all the way up to the top. If you land at the top of a grouchy goblin, you'll have to move all the way down to his toes.

❤ Good luck! The winner is the person who gets their counter to the home square first.

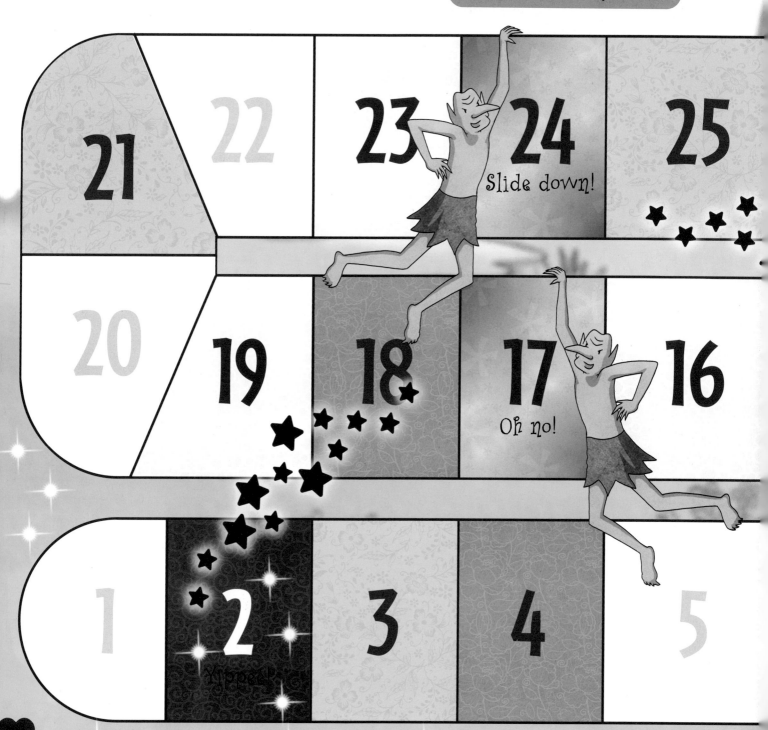

21 22 23 24 Slide down! 25

20 19 18 17 Oh no! 16

1 2 Yippee! 3 4 5

Vain Villain

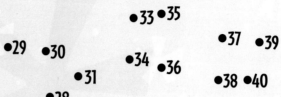

Jack Frost thinks he's so handsome, he's decided to fill this page with a picture of himself! Join up the dots to complete the baddie's jagged beard and frozen hair.

Colour Jack in using icy shades, then draw some lightning bolts around his face.

• 32

• 33 • 35

• 29 • 30

• 37 • 39

• 34 • 36

• 38 • 40

• 31

• 28

• 27

• 26

• 25 • 24

• 41

• 42 • 43

• 44

• 23

• 21 • 22

• 20

• 46

• 45

• 19

• 18

• 17

• 47 • 48

• 16 • 15

• 49

• 13

• 1

• 14

• 3 • 2

• 11

• 5

• 4

• 9 • 7

• 12

• 6

• 10

• 8

26

Style Challenge

Help Miley the Stylist Fairy design something for Keira the Film Star Fairy to wear to her grand fairy film premiere. Can you design a beautiful new outfit for her?

Now choose your prettiest pens and pencils to colour Keira in!

Meet Zadie the
Sewing Fairy

I can make all kinds of
magic with my needle
and thread!

Personality
Resourceful
and neat.

Favourite
fairy friend
Selena the
Sleepover Fairy.

Best crafts
project
A polka-dot
patchwork quilt.

Magical
object
A sparkly golden
thimble.

Favourite
place in
Fairyland
Backstage at Fairyland
fashion shows.

Most
trusted magic
Zadie's special spell
helps everyone to sew
beautifully.

Fairy outfit
Zadie stitches all of her own
clothes. Her amazing sewing
skills make sure everything fits
perfectly! The fairy is especially
proud of her tailored pink
waistcoat and stylish shorts.

When a naughty
goblin snatched
Zadie's magic
thimble, he suddenly
discovered how to
sew! The cheeky
thing stitched himself
a bright green
pinstriped suit and
matching hat.

Zadie's Pretty Pincushion

Zadie's fairy pincushion is ever so handy – it slips on her wrist so she never loses her needles and pins. Would you like to make one, too? Choose your favourite fairy colours, then get stitching!

1

With your chalk and ruler, measure out an 8cm x 6cm rectangle on one of the felt pieces. Ask a grown-up to help you cut it out.

2

Take the second piece of felt and measure out a 7cm x 5cm rectangle. Draw a 6cm x 4cm rectangle on the cereal packet. Ask a grown-up to help you cut these out, too.

3

Lay the bigger piece of felt on a clean table, then place the second piece on top so that it sits neatly in the centre.

Needles, scissors and pins are sharp. Never use them on your own.

4

Thread a needle with the yarn. Carefully sew up three sides of the small piece of felt so that it sits on the big piece like a pocket.

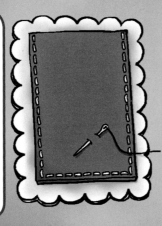

5

Slot the card into the pocket to rest against the bigger piece of fabric. Pop some stuffing inside. Sew the pincushion shut.

Try trimming the edges of the felt with wavy scissors to make it look even more enchanting!

6

Wrap a piece of elastic around your wrist. When you have a length that fits, carefully cut it to size.

7

Stitch both ends of the elastic to the back of the felt. Your fairy pincushion is ready to wear!

Animal Magic

Kirsty and Rachel's visit to the Fairyland Nature Reserve was truly unforgettable – who'd have thought so many amazing wild animals lived and roamed there? The Baby Animal Rescue Fairies are passionate about caring for these creatures and giving them the freedom they deserve...

Koala fact
The closest relatives of the koala are wombats, not bears!

Anna the Arctic Fox Fairy

Anna took Kirsty and Rachel all the way up to the North Pole on a quest to find a stolen Arctic fox called Dazzle. Miko, a brave Inuit boy, chased Jack Frost on a husky-drawn sleigh, determined to set the fox free.

Arctic fox fact
These foxes survive in temperatures as low as -50°C!

Kimberley the Koala Fairy

Her heart fluttered when a mean goblin stole a baby koala called Kiki and took her back to Jack Frost's Ice Castle. Jack's frozen land was far too cold for the baby animal and there were no eucalyptus leaves for her to eat.

Mae the Panda Fairy

She uses her magical key ring to look after all baby pandas. She helped saved a little cub called Pan Pan from being taken to Jack Frost's private zoo. The creature was so sweet, he even melted the heart of a goblin!

Savannah the Zebra Fairy

She was dismayed to spot a stampede of frightened zebras being chased by Jack Frost's goblins. One poor baby struggled to keep up. Luckily Savannah was there to help little Ziggy stay out of harm's way!

Zebra fact
Every zebra has a completely unique pattern of stripes on its body!

Meerkat fact
There can be up to 40 meerkats in one family.

Mara the Meerkat Fairy
She called on Kirsty and Rachel to protect a whole colony of desert meerkats. The girls fell in love with an adorable baby meerkat called Missy. She had little black-ringed eyes, soft brown fur and tiny ears.

Rosie the Honey Bear Fairy
She flew to the human world when she found out that a baby honey bear had gone missing. Kirsty, Rachel and a swarm of bumblebees rushed to return Billy to his mama bear.

Honey bear fact
Honey bears are the smallest of all the bears.

Tiger fact
Tigers are the largest species of wild cat in the world.

Panda fact
Baby panda cubs are born hairless. They also have their eyes closed.

Kitty the Tiger Fairy
She is devoted to tiny tigers! Three cubs needed the fairy's help when Jack Frost started causing trouble near their tropical home. Stripes and his brother Tig got separated from their little cub sister, Sheba.

Jack Frost and the Goblins A-Z

Jack Frost and his naughty gang of goblins have taken over these pages. They really would do anything to steal the fairies' limelight! This awful alphabet will tell you all you need to know about the mischievous meanies – read with care!

A

Animals
Although he's a meanie, Jack does like some animals. His pet snow goose is very precious.

B

Band
Jack thinks his pop group – Frosty and his Gobolicious Band – are the best!

C

Cloak
Jack never goes out without his cloak billowing around his shoulders.

D

Dogs
Goblins might look big and tough, but they are terrified of dogs, no matter how small!

E

Eating
The goblins are such greedy guts that Kirsty and Rachel are often able to thwart their naughty plans by leaving snacks in their path.

F

Fairies
Jack and his goblins can't even say the word without adding a 'pesky' or 'rotten' in front of it!

G

Green
All goblins are bright green, from the points of their long ears to the very tips of their ugly toes.

H

Human world
Jack often comes here to try to spoil things for the fairies!

I

Ice Castle
Jack Frost's enormous home is forged out of solid ice.

J

Jubilee
When Jack heard about Queen Titania and King Oberon's Jubilee, he was taken over with jealousy.

K

Kirsty & Rachel
Goblins grimace when they see Kirsty and Rachel. The best friends would do anything to protect the fairies, much to Jack Frost's dismay!

L M N O P

L — Lake
Outside the Ice Castle is a frozen lake. Jack keeps a small part melted for his snow goose to paddle in.

M — Magical Objects
A fairy's magical object is the key to her special powers. Jack Frost is always trying to steal them to take their magic for himself!

N — Noses
Goblins have twisted and pointy noses.

O — Ocean
Jack hates the ocean, because he can't swim.

P — Pogwurzel
Pogwurzels aren't real, but goblins are still scared of them!

Q — Queen Titania and King Oberon
Jack Frost gets very angry with the Fairyland royals. The silly Ice Lord can't bear to think that Queen Titania and King Oberon might be more important than he is!

R — Rainspell Island
It was here that Jack trapped the Rainbow Fairies – the sisters in charge of keeping the world bright.

S — Spells
Jack Frost uses his powerful wand to cast mean spells on the fairies.

T — Throne
Alone in the Ice Castle, Jack Frost sits on his frozen throne.

U — Unicorn
Jack Frost stole Leona the Unicorn Fairy's pet unicorn, Twisty.

V — Vain
Jack Frost is so vain, he stole Alexa the Fashion Reporter Fairy's magical pen to write an interview with himself!

W — Warty
Goblins all have horrible lumpy warts on their long green noses and toeses!

X — X-tra sneaky!
No matter what they do, the fairies can't persuade Jack Frost to give up his sneaky ways.

Y — Year
When Jack stole the Weather Fairies' feathers, he had his magic taken away for a year as punishment.

Z — Zzzzzzzz
Whenever Jack Frost isn't looking, the goblins try to sneak a nap. They are so lazy and afraid of hard work!

Shiny beads, glossy pearls and twinkly charms – let's get creative!

Meet Josie the Jewellery-Making Fairy

Personality
Smiley and thoughtful.

Favourite fairy friend
Claudia the Accessories Fairy.

Magical object
A pink ribbon with glittery beads.

Best crafts project
Friendship bracelets with rainbow-coloured beads.

Most trusted magic
It's always fun to make gifts and trinkets when Josie is around!

Favourite place in Fairyland
The palace ballroom – Josie loves the crystal chandeliers!

Fairy outfit
Josie knows just how to set off her lace-edged top – with beads, bangles and bracelets! Her eye-catching green necklace is extra-special. It's the first piece of jewellery she ever made.

Carys's Silver Shop was in chaos when Josie's magical necklace went missing. Kirsty and Rachel found the fairy inside a jewellery box, then helped her put things right again.

Josie's Jangly Bangles

Josie can often be spied fluttering around Fairyland, delivering her handmade trinkets. These colourful bangles make such a thoughtful gift.

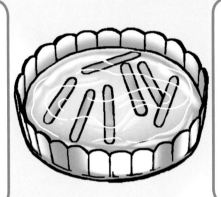

1
Ask a grown-up to boil a kettle, then lay your lolly sticks down in a heatproof dish.

2
When the kettle is ready, ask your helper to pour hot water over the lolly sticks. Leave the sticks to soak for 45 minutes.

3
Carefully pick the lolly sticks out of the water and bend with your fingers. If they don't curve easily in your hand, put the sticks back in the dish and do steps 1 and 2 again.

Don't use a kettle on your own – always ask a grown-up to help.

4
Gently bend each stick into a curve. Then slide each into a thin glass so that it holds its shape. Leave the glass on the windowsill or beside a radiator to dry out overnight.

5
When the curved sticks are dry, slip them out of the glass. If there are any rough edges, sand the sticks with an old emery board.

Why not pick pink and gold to match Josie's magical necklace?

6
Spread out some newspaper and then paint the bangles in pretty colours.

7
When the bangles are dry, it's time to work your fairy magic! Stick on some sparkly gem shapes, sequins and glitter.

35

I Spy Fairies!

It's a busy day in the Palace Kitchens – it's Queen Titania's birthday! There are going to be parties all over Fairyland. Peep at the happy scene, then answer each of the quiz questions.

Find out if you're right on Page 61

1. What colour is Melodie's apron?
_____

2. What type of fairy are Ruby and Sky?
_____

3. Who is doing the dishes?
_____

4. How many helper bees can you find?
_____

5. What are Polly and Jasmine doing?
_____

6. How many layers of cake are there?
_____

7. What's inside the starry gift box?
_____

8. Who is peeping through the window?
_____

9. How many cupcakes can you see?
_____

Part 2

Diamonds and Ice

Kirsty and Rachel felt their hearts skip with excitement. Gabriella waved her magic wand, then spoke in a whisper.

Friends of fairies, we believe,
It's time to save this New Year's Eve!

As soon as her spell was finished, a swoosh of sparkles burst out of her wand, and Kirsty and Rachel felt themselves shrink to fairy size.

"It's happening," cried Rachel, pointing at Kirsty. A pair of wings had appeared on her back! Rachel looked over her shoulder. She had them, too!

Suddenly the air turned icy cold. When the sparkles faded, they found themselves in a snowy, mountainous land. Two green faces peered down at them from a jagged fortress.

"I know where we are," said Kirsty. "That's Jack Frost's Ice Castle!"

"And those are his goblin servants," piped up Rachel.

Chrissie nodded. "King Oberon and Queen Titania asked us to bring you here," she explained. "They've made a new year's resolution to try and be friends with Jack Frost, starting tonight at the Icicle Extravaganza."

"What's that?" wondered Kirsty.

Gabriella burst into a glittering smile.

"It's a magical concert filled with dancers and fairy lights. On the stroke of midnight Queen Titania casts a good luck spell for the year ahead."

"Their Majesties want to invite Jack Frost to host the party," added Chrissie. "As a sign of friendship."

Gabriella sighed. "We've asked him, but he won't even consider it! Would you try?"

Rachel peeped at her watch. It was nearly six o'clock already!

"All right," she said bravely. Kirsty and Rachel fluttered into Jack Frost's castle. As soon as the Ice Lord spotted them, his face broke into a scowl.

"More pesky fairies!" he groaned.

"You're not wanted here," harrumphed a goblin, shaking a fist at them.

"That's a shame," called down Kirsty. "This would be the perfect venue for an Icicle Extravaganza."

Rachel winked at Kirsty. "Yes," she continued, "and the host would be the star of the show."

Jack Frost's ears pricked up.

"What's that?" he said.

"Such an honour," sighed Rachel. "But if you're not interested…"

Jack Frost leapt to his feet, lifting his wand. Icy-blue bolts whizzed in all directions.

"Of course I am interested!" he yelled. "What are you waiting for, goblins? We've got a party to organise."

Turn to page 54 to read about the glittering Icicle Extravaganza!

A Magical Mystery!

Kirsty and Rachel were roller-skating in Tippington when they came across the most wonderful fairy! Can you guess who it was? Read the clues, look at the silhouette, then fill in the mystery fairy's name.

Clues

She is the keeper of the True Love Crown.

She carries a trailing bouquet of flowers.

Her gown is made of delicate ivory silk.

The fairy's name is...

_____
_____

Still not sure?
Here's an extra clue. All of these letters feature in her name.

K A E L A D
W E Y G N D
O R I T

Find out if you're right on Page 61

40

Interview with Alexandra the Royal Baby Fairy

Royal babies are so precious. The whole of Fairyland was excited to hear that one was on the way! Alexandra the Royal Baby Fairy couldn't wait to meet the tiny prince or princess. Let's find out more about this special royal guardian.

Hello Alexandra, how long have you been a Royal Baby Fairy?
Ever since I can remember! I was taught by my kindly fairy godmother.

Do you have a magical object?
Yes, a tinkling rattle shaped out of the finest silver. My magic wouldn't work without it.

What is your fairy job?
To make sure that royal babies carry out their duties and have a magical childhood!

It sounds wonderful!
Why, yes, usually it is enchanting. All babies are adorable, especially little princes and princesses! If only Jack Frost and his goblins didn't keep trying to spoil things...

What have they done?
As soon as he found out that there was going to be a new royal baby, Jack Frost started hatching naughty plans. He plotted to take the baby back to his Ice Castle – poor little mite!

Why would Jack Frost want to have a baby in his frozen land?
He wanted to teach it to play tricks on the fairies and cause even more trouble in Fairyland. Trust Jack Frost to find ways of making mischief!

How did you know something was wrong?
When Foster the Stork failed to make his delivery on time, I knew the baby needed my help.

Thank goodness you were there to save the day!
Not just me – I couldn't have done it without my dear friends Kirsty and Rachel. As soon as the mischief began, I travelled to the human world to find them. The girls were having a day out at Norwood Palace.

What a relief! Do any other fairies ever help you look after the royal baby?
The fairies are all so kind, but Jennifer the Babysitter Fairy is extra special. She often flutters by to lend a hand! Jennifer spends her days working in the Fairyland Nursery, so she knows just how to look after babies and toddlers.

I'm happiest when I'm painting wonderful works of art!

Meet Violet the Painting Fairy

Personality
Bubbly and playful.

Favourite fairy friend
Madeleine the Cookie Fairy.

Magical object
A swishy fairy paintbrush.

Best crafts project
A colourful mural in the Fairyland nursery.

Most trusted magic
Violet helps fairies and humans paint lovely landscapes and pretty portraits.

Favourite place in Fairyland
The rolling hills above Fairyland. It's the best place to sit and paint.

Fairy outfit
Violet's boots and dungarees are just right for a busy fairy artist! If she gets too messy, she waves her wand and any paint splats disappear. Violet always keeps a spare paint brush in her ponytail.

When poor Violet lost her magical paintbrush, some old friends fluttered in to help. The kindly Rainbow Fairies flew to Jack Frost's Ice Castle and made him give the brush back.

Violet's Magical Rainbow Paint

Violet was so thrilled that the Rainbow Fairies could help save her precious paintbrush! This magical painting is so eye-catching – all you need are some watercolours and a black crayon.

You will need:
- ☐ Thin white card
- ☐ Watercolour paints
- ☐ Black wax crayon
- ☐ Old newspapers
- ☐ Paintbrush
- ☐ Cocktail stick

1
Spread out some old newspaper. Carefully paint rainbow stripes all across the card. Start with a swish of red at the top, then work all your way down to violet. Make sure that every part of the card is covered with paint. Then leave your card to dry completely.

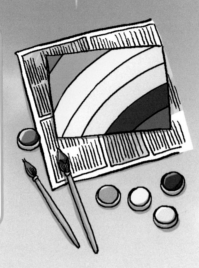

2
Take a black crayon and colour over your painting. Keep going until the while sheet of card is black.

3
Now use a cocktail stick to scratch a picture into the black. The crayon will magically fall away, revealing beautiful rainbow colours underneath!

There are seven colours in the rainbow: red, orange, yellow, green, blue, indigo and violet.

Take some more card, then play with different paint colours and patterns. Will you scratch away the crayon to reveal Queen Titania dressed in a beautiful rainbow skirt, or choose to fill your card with pretty coloured bows and love hearts?

Silly Speak

It looks like Jack Frost has been causing trouble again! Someone has jumbled these fairy quotes into the wrong order. Read the words, look at the pictures, then draw lines to reveal who said what.

Florene the Friendship Fairy

Juliet the Valentine Fairy

B. "My magical object is a gold tiara with a red jewel in the centre."

A. "Do you like my pink shell ankle bracelets? They jangle as I swim!"

Demi the Happy Days Fairy

D. "My favourite day is October 31st – as long as people don't get too scared!"

C. "I have three precious objects – a memory book, a ribbon and a friendship bracelet."

Shannon the Ocean Fairy

E. "I'm always extra busy on February 14th!"

Trixie the Halloween Fairy

F. "I have a moonstone ring, an endless coin and a magical pouch."

Tamara the Tooth Fairy

Royal Rhymes

Her majesty Queen Titania is terribly upset – her magic wand has gone missing! Without it, the queen's fairy powers will start to ebb away. Can you help Elizabeth the Jubilee Fairy cast a wishing spell to get it back again?

A fairy queen without her magic,
Is nothing short of truly tragic!
We loyal subjects shall not slack,
Until we get the object back.

River deep and mountain high,
In every corner we shall pry,
Forest, valley, stream and pond,
We will find your fairy wand.

Elizabeth has written the first two verses of the spell. Find a pretty pen and see if you can write a third one. Make each line as magical as you can!

_____

_____

_____

_____

ink

Fairy Hide-and-Seek

Fairies love playing fun games! Lauren the Puppy Fairy and her pet puppy have finished counting and are ready for a fresh round of hide-and-seek. Can you help her find the seven fairy hiders?

Tyra the Dress Designer Fairy

Olympia the Games Fairy

Find out if you're right on Page 61

Francesca the Football Fairy

Edie the Garden Fairy

Anya the Cuddly Creatures Fairy

Kitty the Tiger Fairy

Lila & Myla the Twins Fairies

Meet Libby the Story-Writing Fairy

Close your eyes and think of a story!

Personality
Dreamy and imaginative.

Favourite fairy friend
Hannah the Happy Ever After Fairy.

Magical object
A notebook tied with golden thread.

Best crafts project
A magical story Libby wrote especially for the Princess Fairies.

Most trusted magic
Libby's magic is there to inspire everyone to write exciting new stories.

Favourite place in Fairyland
Her cosy toadstool bedroom.

Libby's dress shimmers with tiny silver stars – it looks so pretty as she flutters through the air! When the air gets chilly, Libby pops on a waterfall cardigan in the softest shade of baby pink.

Although the goblins shouldn't have taken Libby's notebook, she didn't stay cross with them for long. The sweet fairy gave each one a bound copy of their story to take home and treasure.

Libby's Secret Stories

Libby's imagination is always fizzing with new story ideas! She's started writing a new one in her notebook – can you help her complete it? Close your eyes, whisk yourself off to Fairyland, then fill in the blank spaces.

(Title)
_____

a fairy story by Libby and

(Name)
_____

It was a .... morning in Fairyland. .... the .... Fairy sat up in bed and gently unfurled her wings.

She peeped up at her fairy calendar. "Oh no!" she exclaimed. "I'm late! I'm supposed to be meeting .... for breakfast in five minutes. She popped on her favourite ...., brushed her hair, then fluttered out of the door.

By the time she arrived at ...., her friend wasn't there! The fairy looked inside and asked around, but no one had seen her.

"Maybe she's still at home?" she wondered. "I'll take a picnic breakfast round to her house, just in case." She packed some .... into a hamper, and then set off. Soon she was flying over the emerald green hills of Fairyland.

When she arrived, she flitted up to the bedroom window. The .... were still shut! The little fairy smiled, then rang the bell.

When her friend opened the door, she was still wearing her ....! "Looks like I'm not the only one who's late this morning!" said the little fairy happily.

The friends went inside and shared out the breakfast, eating delicious .... and .... "Thank you so much," said her friend. "It's been a magical morning!"

Top of the Class!

Carly the Schoolfriend Fairy is there to make sure that everyone's school days are interesting and fun. Last week she set herself a piece of homework – to collect her top ten rules for making the most out of school. Read Carly's tips and share them with your friends.

Be prepared
Take five minutes every morning to check your school bag before you leave the house. Then you'll never be worried about forgetting things!

Look your best
When we dress smartly, it helps us feel alert and ready to learn! Check that your shoes are shiny and your clothes are neat.

Try new things
There is so much to do at school, both in and out of lessons! It's always fun to take up new hobbies, and meet even more people!

Don't worry about being good at everything
Even if you find a subject difficult, try your best and have a go. You'll feel proud of yourself afterwards, whatever happens!

Be yourself
Try not to worry about being popular or fashionable – just be yourself! Your friends will love you just the way you are!

Smile!
Try to be kind to everybody and always smiley – it's a great way of showing the class what a friendly, happy person you are!

Make lots of friends
Try to chat and play with lots of different people. It's good to be loyal to your old friends, but there's always room for new playmates, too.

Share your ideas
Try and put your hand up when you can, even if you feel shy. It doesn't matter if you get it wrong – every time you do it you'll get a little braver.

Get your homework out of the way
If you have spellings to learn or maths to do, try and get it done as soon as you get home. Then you will be free to have fun!

Tell a teacher
If you see anyone being hurtful or unkind to someone else, tell a teacher. The adult will know what to do to put things right again.

Through the Looking Glass

Demi the Dressing-Up Fairy loves getting glammed up in front of her mirror. Give her clothes some colour and sparkle so she looks pretty as a picture!

Will you give Demi a pink ruffled skirt and matching pumps, or try something new? It's up to you!

Perfect Pairs

Lila and Myla the Twins Fairies know that all the best things come in pairs! Naughty Jack Frost has got these objects into a muddle. Draw lines to match each picture up to its perfect pair.

Find out if you're right on Page 61

Midnight Maze

Some goblins never learn! These green meanies have made off with Morgan the Midnight Fairy's bag of magical night dust. Unless she gets it back, there will be chaos from dusk to dawn! Show Morgan the best way through the shadows and stars. Use a pen or pencil to draw a line along the best route.

Find out if you're right on Page 61

Diamonds and Ice

Chrissie flew over to the frozen pond and touched it. Magically, King Oberon and Queen Titania appeared on the surface!

"Good work, Kirsty and Rachel," declared the king.

"The fairies are already on their way," smiled Queen Titania. "See you at the concert!"

And suddenly, in a flurry of hugs and hellos, the fairies appeared!

"One, two…" called Vanessa the Dance Steps Fairy to her dancers.

Over on the frozen lake, Isla the Ice Star Fairy was twirling around.

"We're nearly ready!" cried Una the Concert Fairy.

"It's going to be wonderful," said Kirsty happily.

It was time for the Icicle Extravaganza. At a nod from Jack Frost, a thousand fairy lights lit up.

Rachel gasped as she looked down at her clothes. Both girls were suddenly wearing sparkling party dresses!

The king and queen glided into view on a golden sleigh. They waved to the partygoers, then took their places beside Jack Frost.

The concert was amazing. They saw the

ice dancers and the Pop Star Fairies, but the biggest round of applause went to the goblins!

A frog trumpeter sounded the royal fanfare. It was one minute to midnight. The audience fell silent as Queen Titania placed a sparkling diamond tiara on her head. A breathtaking shimmer of fireworks exploded in the night sky.

Farewell to old, hello to new,
Joyous times I wish to you!

But as the clock struck twelve, a sulky voice rang out of the crowd.

"Bah!" shouted Jack Frost, pointing a bony finger. "I don't wish you joyous times! This is meant to be my party, not yours. How come you get to say the new year's spell?"

The grumpy Ice Lord swished his cloak and stormed inside.

"Trust Jack Frost!" whispered Kirsty. "We should've known his good behaviour wouldn't last!"

Rachel giggled. At least her new year's resolution had come true – the friends had shared another enchanting adventure with the fairies!

The End

Meet Roxie the Baking Fairy

I always sing songs as I make and bake!

Personality
Sweet and friendly.

Favourite fairy friend
Angelica the Angel Fairy.

Magical object
A star-shaped cookie cutter.

Best crafts project
Roxie's birthday biscuits are famous all over Fairyland!

Most trusted magic
Baking is bound to be a sweet success when Roxie's nearby!

Favourite place in Fairyland
The palace kitchens.

The frilly net beneath Roxie's dress makes it puff up just like a cupcake! Her gorgeous pink frock is decorated with sugar sprinkles. Zadie the Sewing Fairy helped Roxie sew each one on.

After Kirsty and Rachel got Roxie's magical cookie cutter back from the goblins, the friends were in a rush. The fairy helped the girls bake for the Crafts Week exhibition on Rainspell Island.

Honey

Roxie's Cookie Wands

Roxie's fairy kitchen is a wonderful place to be. There really is nothing better than the warm smell of biscuits baking in the oven! These scrumptious cookie wands are made out of shortbread and lolly sticks.

You will need:
- [ ] 200g butter
- [ ] 300g plain flour
- [ ] 1 tsp vanilla extract
- [ ] 100g caster sugar
- [ ] 2 eggs
- [ ] 24 lolly sticks, soaked in water
- [ ] A star-shaped cookie cutter
- [ ] 125g granulated sugar
- [ ] Food colouring

1

Cut the butter into chunks. Add the flour, vanilla extract and caster sugar. Mix the ingredients together until they bind into a sweet dough.

2

Sprinkle flour on the worktop, then roll out the dough until it is as thick as your finger. Use the cookie cutter to press out star shapes.

Ask a grown-up to heat the oven to 190°C/375°F/ Gas Mark 5.

3

Push a lolly stick firmly into each star. Place the shapes on a baking tray, then pop them in the fridge for 15 minutes to chill.

4

Put the wands into the oven for about 10-12 minutes, until they turn golden brown. Then leave them to cool completely.

5

Ask your grown-up to help you separate the eggs into yolks and whites. You won't need the yolks, so set them aside in a different bowl.

6

Add a few drops of your favourite food colouring to the granulated sugar. Stir it all together until the colour is even throughout.

7

Use a pastry brush to paint every cookie star with egg white. Sprinkle on the coloured sugar. Once dry, your wands are ready to enjoy!

Jingle Belle

Robyn the Christmas Party Fairy needs a new outfit for a party in the Fairyland Palace Ballroom. Will you help Tyra the Dress Designer Fairy create something for her to wear? Find a pencil and get to work!

Fairy Facts or Frosty Fibs?

Georgie the Royal Prince Fairy makes sure that special royal events go off without a hitch! This page is all about the glittering, golden fairy. Some of these sentences are fairy facts, but others are frosty fibs. Can you work out which are which?

Georgie's symbols are tiny gold crowns.

Beautiful Wings
Georgie flutters around Fairyland on a gorgeous pair of gossamer wings tinted lime green.

1. Georgie the Royal Prince Fairy's magical object is a signet ring.
Fact ☐
Fib ☐

2. Georgie carries a slipper on a velvet cushion.
Fact ☐
Fib ☐

3. Kirsty and Rachel first met Georgie when they were getting ready for a palace garden party.
Fact ☐
Fib ☐

4. Georgie's yellow dress is decorated with delicate golden polka dots.
Fact ☐
Fib ☐

5. When she waves her wand, glittering thrones appear.
Fact ☐
Fib ☐

6. Georgie appeared to invite Kirsty and Rachel to a royal baby naming ceremony.
Fact ☐
Fib ☐

7. Jack Frost didn't cause any trouble at the ceremony, because he was invited.
Fact ☐
Fib ☐

8. At the royal weekend, Kirsty and Rachel got to see five real princesses.
Fact ☐
Fib ☐

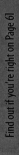

Find out if you're right on Page 61

Dear Fairy Friend,

The time has come for us to flutter
back to Fairyland — thank you so
much for sharing our Annual with us.

Now that you're friends with the
Magical Crafts Fairies, don't forget
to have a go at lots more arty projects.
With your sparkling imagination,
you're sure to make all sorts of
wonderful things!

With love and sweet fairy wishes,

Kayla x Annabelle x Zadie x Josie x
Violet x Libby x Roxie x

Answers

P9

Pop Star Puzzle
Image D

I Spy Fairies!
1. Pink
2. Rainbow Fairies
3. Two birds
4. Five
5. Wrapping presents
6. Four layers of cake
7. A teddy bear
8. A goblin
9. Ten

P36

Wand Wordsearch
P14

E	A	S	T	E	R	E	G	G	N
D	G	N	I	N	T	H	G	I	L
R	I	B	F	T	C	W	G	U	K
Y	P	A	X	S	H	E	L	L	C
I	E	D	M	N	M	K	D	E	I
L	N	H	V	O	L	D	C	P	T
R	O	X	A	Z	N	B	L	T	S
H	E	A	R	T	L	D	O	V	P
J	Z	K	W	Q	S	G	F	I	I
S	N	O	W	F	L	A	K	E	L

A Magical Mystery!
Kate the Royal Wedding Fairy
P40

Belle's Quiz
P21

1. Purple
2. Rachel and Kirsty
3. Hairbrush & a lip gloss
4. A balloon
5. A birthday cake
6. Fairy dust
7. Pink
8. 10

Cross Words
P22

Across/Down answers:
- CLOAK
- ICE
- SNOW GOOSE
- GREEN
- CASTLE
- GOBLINS
- BLUE
- LAKE
- FEET
- FAIRIES
- ICICLE

Silly Speak
P44

Fairy Hide-and-Seek
P46

Perfect Pairs
P52

Midnight Maze
P53

Fairy Facts or Frosty Fibs?
P59

1. Fact
2. Fib
3. Fact
4. Fact
5. Fib
6. Fact
7. Fib
8. Fib

Have you read them all?

The Rainbow Fairies
1. Ruby the Red Fairy ☐
2. Amber the Orange Fairy ☐
3. Saffron the Yellow Fairy ☐
4. Fern the Green Fairy ☐
5. Sky the Blue Fairy ☐
6. Izzy the Indigo Fairy ☐
7. Heather the Violet Fairy ☐

The Weather Fairies
8. Crystal the Snow Fairy ☐
9. Abigail the Breeze Fairy ☐
10. Pearl the Cloud Fairy ☐
11. Goldie the Sunshine Fairy ☐
12. Evie the Mist Fairy ☐
13. Storm the Lightning Fairy ☐
14. Hayley the Rain Fairy ☐

The Party Fairies
15. Cherry the Cake Fairy ☐
16. Melodie the Music Fairy ☐
17. Grace the Glitter Fairy ☐
18. Honey the Sweet Fairy ☐
19. Polly the Party Fun Fairy ☐
20. Phoebe the Fashion Fairy ☐
21. Jasmine the Present Fairy ☐

The Jewel Fairies
22. India the Moonstone Fairy ☐
23. Scarlett the Garnet Fairy ☐
24. Emily the Emerald Fairy ☐
25. Chloe the Topaz Fairy ☐
26. Amy the Amethyst Fairy ☐
27. Sophie the Sapphire Fairy ☐
28. Lucy the Diamond Fairy ☐

The Pet Keeper Fairies
29. Katie the Kitten Fairy ☐
30. Bella the Bunny Fairy ☐
31. Georgia the Guinea Pig Fairy ☐
32. Lauren the Puppy Fairy ☐
33. Harriet the Hamster Fairy ☐
34. Molly the Goldfish Fairy ☐
35. Penny the Pony Fairy ☐

The Fun Day Fairies
36. Megan the Monday Fairy ☐
37. Tallulah the Tuesday Fairy ☐
38. Willow the Wednesday Fairy ☐
39. Thea the Thursday Fairy ☐
40. Freya the Friday Fairy ☐
41. Sienna the Saturday Fairy ☐
42. Sarah the Sunday Fairy ☐

The Petal Fairies
43. Tia the Tulip Fairy ☐
44. Pippa the Poppy Fairy ☐
45. Louise the Lily Fairy ☐
46. Charlotte the Sunflower Fairy ☐
47. Olivia the Orchid Fairy ☐
48. Danielle the Daisy Fairy ☐
49. Ella the Rose Fairy ☐

The Dance Fairies
50. Bethany the Ballet Fairy ☐
51. Jade the Disco Fairy ☐
52. Rebecca the Rock'n'Roll Fairy ☐
53. Tasha the Tap Dance Fairy ☐
54. Jessica the Jazz Fairy ☐
55. Saskia the Salsa Fairy ☐
56. Imogen the Ice Dance Fairy ☐

The Sporty Fairies
57. Helena the Horseriding Fairy ☐
58. Francesca the Football Fairy ☐
59. Zoe the Skating Fairy ☐
60. Naomi the Netball Fairy ☐
61. Samantha the Swimming Fairy ☐
62. Alice the Tennis Fairy ☐
63. Gemma the Gymnastics Fairy ☐

The Music Fairies
64. Poppy the Piano Fairy ☐
65. Ellie the Guitar Fairy ☐
66. Fiona the Flute Fairy ☐
67. Danni the Drum Fairy ☐
68. Maya the Harp Fairy ☐
69. Victoria the Violin Fairy ☐
70. Sadie the Saxophone Fairy ☐

The Magical Animal Fairies
71. Ashley the Dragon Fairy ☐
72. Lara the Black Cat Fairy ☐
73. Erin the Firebird Fairy ☐
74. Rihanna the Seahorse Fairy ☐
75. Sophia the Snow Swan Fairy ☐
76. Leona the Unicorn Fairy ☐
77. Caitlin the Ice Bear Fairy ☐

The Green Fairies
78. Nicole the Beach Fairy ☐
79. Isabella the Air Fairy ☐
80. Edie the Garden Fairy ☐
81. Coral the Reef Fairy ☐
82. Lily the Rainforest Fairy ☐
83. Carrie the Snow Cap Fairy ☐
84. Milly the River Fairy ☐

The Ocean Fairies
85. Ally the Dolphin Fairy ☐
86. Amelie the Seal Fairy ☐
87. Pia the Penguin Fairy ☐
88. Tess the Sea Turtle Fairy ☐
89. Stephanie the Starfish Fairy ☐
90. Whitney the Whale Fairy ☐
91. Courtney the Clownfish Fairy ☐

The Twilight Fairies
92. Ava the Sunset Fairy ☐
93. Lexi the Firefly Fairy ☐
94. Zara the Starlight Fairy ☐
95. Morgan the Midnight Fairy ☐
96. Yasmin the Night Owl Fairy ☐
97. Maisie the Moonbeam Fairy ☐
98. Sabrina the Sweet Dreams Fairy ☐

The Showtime Fairies
99. Madison the Magic Show Fairy ☐
100. Leah the Theatre Fairy ☐
101. Alesha the Acrobat Fairy ☐
102. Darcey the Dance Diva Fairy ☐
103. Taylor the Talent Show Fairy ☐
104. Amelia the Singing Fairy ☐
105. Isla the Ice Star Fairy ☐

The Princess Fairies
106. Honor the Happy Days Fairy ☐
107. Demi the Dressing-Up Fairy ☐
108. Anya the Cuddly Creatures Fairy ☐
109. Elisa the Adventure Fairy ☐
110. Lizzie the Sweet Treats Fairy ☐
111. Maddie the Playtime Fairy ☐
112. Eva the Enchanted Ball Fairy ☐

The Pop Star Fairies
113. Jessie the Lyrics Fairy ☐
114. Adele the Singing Coach Fairy ☐
115. Vanessa the Dance Steps Fairy ☐
116. Miley the Stylist Fairy ☐
117. Frankie the Make-Up Fairy ☐
118. Rochelle the Star Spotter Fairy ☐
119. Una the Concert Fairy ☐

The Fashion Fairies
120. Miranda the Beauty Fairy ☐
121. Claudia the Accessories Fairy ☐
122. Tyra the Dress Designer Fairy ☐
123. Alexa the Fashion Reporter Fairy ☐
124. Matilda the Hair Stylist Fairy ☐
125. Brooke the Photographer Fairy ☐
126. Lola the Fashion Fairy ☐

The Sweet Fairies
127. Lottie the Lollipop Fairy ☐
128. Esme the Ice Cream Fairy ☐
129. Coco the Cupcake Fairy ☐
130. Clara the Chocolate Fairy ☐
131. Madeleine the Cookie Fairy ☐
132. Layla the Candyfloss Fairy ☐
133. Nina the Birthday Cake Fairy ☐

The Baby Animal Rescue Fairies
134. Mae the Panda Fairy ☐
135. Kitty the Tiger Fairy ☐
136. Mara the Meerkat Fairy ☐
137. Savannah the Zebra Fairy ☐
138. Kimberley the Koala Fairy ☐
139. Rosie the Honey Bear Fairy ☐
140. Anna the Arctic Fox Fairy ☐

The Magical Crafts Fairies
141. Kayla the Pottery Fairy ☐
142. Annabelle the Drawing Fairy ☐
143. Zadie the Sewing Fairy ☐
144. Josie the Jewellery-Making Fairy ☐
145. Violet the Painting Fairy ☐
146. Libby the Story-Writing Fairy ☐
147. Roxie the Baking Fairy ☐